TALES OF

Pictures and Text by **Aki Izumoi**

JAPANESE GODS

Translated by **Jules Kankoe Aduayom**

にっぽんの かみさまの おはなし

いずもい あき・えとぶん　アデュアヨム カンコエ・やく

産經新聞社

Book Design by
Yoshihiro Shimizu   Yoshiko Sano
清水良洋・佐の佳子

こどものえほん
おとなのえほん
こどもにも　おとなにも
しあわせを　はこんでくる
えほんです

A picture book for children
A picture book for parents
This is an illustrated book that will delight
children and adults alike

うちゅうのはじまり （1）

とおい　とおい
いつ　はじまったかも
わからない　おおむかし
うちゅうのかみ
あめのみなかぬしさまが
あらわれました。

たかい　たかい
そらのうえに
ふかい　ふかい
ちの　そこから
あっちにも　こっちにも。

そして　いまも
あめのみなかぬしさまは
ずっと　あらわれつづけ
はたらきつづけて　います。
いま　あなたの　まわりにも
あなたのなかにも
ほら　よいことばかりの
かみさまは　いらっしゃる！
めには　みえないけれど
うちゅうのかみさまは
いらっしゃるのです。

THE BEGINNING OF THE UNIVERSE (1)

Long, long ago,
We do not know when, but the god of the universe,
"Ameno-Minakanushi" appeared.
High, high in the heavens,
Deep, deep under the earth,
The god of the universe is everywhere,
Living and working.
Right now, around you and within you.
Look! The god of good deeds lives.
The god of the universe is invisible;
But the god does exist.

うちゅうの　　はじまり（2）

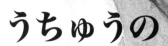

どこまでも　つづく　そらには
むくもくと　くもが　いっぱい！

どこまでも　つづく　うみは
どぶん　ざぶんと　なみが　どろが
さわいでいました。

その　そらのうえから
うみのなかから
うちゅうのかみさまは
ほほえみました。

THE BEGINNING OF THE UNIVERSE (2)

In the immense sky,
There were huge clusters of clouds,
In the vast ocean, waves and mud splashed.
From above the sky,
From below the ocean
The god of the universe smiled.

おや！　どろのうえに
ちく　ちく　ちっと
かびのような　ものが
はえだしました。

くさや　あしの　めも
かおを　だしました。

つののある　いきものも
うまれて　きました。
いろいろ　いろいろと。

「すごいなー」
「すばらしいなー」

In the mud, something like
mold started growing.
Grass and reeds and
Living creatures came into being.
Life of many types and shapes
"Wonderful and various they were!!"

うちゅうのはじまり（3）

うちゅうの　かみさまは
いざなぎ・いざなみ　という
おとこのかみさまと
めがみさまの　ふたりに

「おおぞらのしたに
ふたりで
ちからをあわせて
しあわせのくにを
つくるのですよ」
と　おっしゃって

THE BEGINNING OF THE UNIVERSE (3)

There were a god named Izanagi and a goddess named Izanami.
The god of the universe told them to join forces and
create a country full of happiness under the sky.
He gave them Amenonuboko, a spear with mysterious power.
Izanagi and Izanami were delighted;
They boarded a cloud and took off together.
Izanagi dispersed the dark clouds with his spear and went ahead.

ふしぎなちからのある
"あめのぬぼこ"を
わたされました。

「ありがとう」
いざなぎ・いざなみさまは
よろこんで
くもに　のって
しゅっぱーつ！

いざなぎさまは
くろくもを　ほこで
ちりぢりに　おいはらって
すすみました。

うちゅうのはじまり　（4）

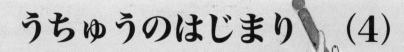

なないろの
うつくしい　はしが
うかんでいました。

いざなぎ・いざなみさまは
てを　つないで
はしにあがりました。

なぎさまは　ほこで
くもの　したを
こーろ　こーろと
かきまわして
ほこを
ひきあげました。

THE BEGINNING OF THE UNIVERSE (4)

In the sky, a beautiful 7-color rainbow bridge appeared before
Izanagi and Izanami.
Hand in hand, they stepped up on to it.
With the spear, Izanagi stirred the clouds.
He raised his arm, and drops fell from the tip of the spear.
These drops hardened and formed a big island.
"Done! Onogoro island!"
"Oh! How beautiful it is!!"
The two gods descended to the island.

ほこの　さきから　ぽとり　ぽとりと
おちた　しずくが　かたまって
おおきな　しまが　できました。

「おのごろじまが　できた！」
「まあ！　すばらしい！」

ふたりの　かみさまは
おのごろじまに　おりました。

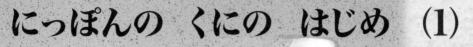

にっぽんの くにの はじめ （1）

いざなぎ・いざなみさまは
てんに とどく
たかい はしらを たてて

「おのごろじまを ありがとう」
うちゅうのかみさまに
おれいを いいました。
せっせと はたらいて
ひろーい ごてんも たてました。

「うれしいなー」「たのしいなー」
ふたりは はしらの まわりを
なぎさまは ひだりから
なみさまは みぎから まわりました。

THE BEGINNING OF JAPAN (1)

Izanagi and Izanami erected a pillar tall enough to reach Heaven.
They thanked the god of the universe for the creation of the island.
They started working and built a big palace.
"How joyful!" "How happy!"
They chanted and turned around the pillar,
Izanagi from the left and Izanami from the right.
They praised each other, saying:
"You are a beautiful goddess Izanami!"
"You are a great god, Izanagi!"
They joined hands and slept happily.

「なみひめは　うつくしい！」
「りっぱな　かみさまだこと　なぎさまは！」

ふたりの　かみさまは
てを　つないで
なかよく　ねむりました。

にっぽんの　くにの　はじめ　（2）

「おはよう」
「ごきげんよう」

いざなぎ・いざなみさまは
めが　さめて　びっくりしました。

あおい　うみから
しまが　にこにこと
かおを　だしていました。
いくつも　いくつも。

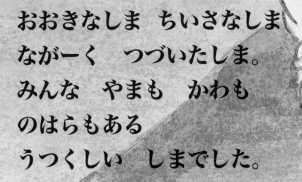

おおきなしま　ちいさなしま
ながーく　つづいたしま。
みんな　やまも　かわも
のはらもある
うつくしい　しまでした。

「すばらしい　くにが　うまれた！」
「よかったね　うれしいね」

　　むかし　むかし
　　にっぽんの　くにが　うまれたときの　おはなしです。

THE BEGINNING OF JAPAN (2)

"Hello!" "Good Morning!"
Izanagi and Izanami woke up in great amazement.
So many, many islands - big ones and small ones
were forming in the blue ocean.
All of them were filled with mountains, rivers and plains.
They were beautiful islands!
"A great nation was born!!"

"How nice! How wonderful!!"
This is the story of the beginning of Japan long, long ago.

かみさまたちの　　たんじょう

なぎさまと　なみさまは
おひさまが　かがやいているときは
よく　はたらき
おほしさまが　ひかる　ころは
なかよく　ねむりました。

THE BIRTH OF THE GODS

Izanagi and Izanami worked hard under the sun during the day.
And at night they slept under the stars.
A son and a daughter were born to them.
And a god for every creature;
One to protect the house,
One for the roof top, one for the field, one for the mountain and
Another one for the ocean;
Gods for everything that can be seen and heard, were born.
"Avarice and violence are not good indeed."
A cheerful and wonderful country was born.

おとこの　かみさまも
おんなの　かみさまも　うまれました。

いえを　まもるかみ　やねのかみ
のはらのかみ　やまのかみ　うみのかみ
めに　みえるもの　みみに　きこえるもの
みんなの　かみが　うまれました。

「よくばり　けんかは
よくないね」
にぎやかな　たのしい
よいくにに　なりました。

もえる　ひの　かみの　たんじょう

いざなみさまは
おしまいに　ぼうぼうと　もえる
ひの　かみを　うみました。
やけどをして　しんで　しまいました。

いざなぎさまも　こどもの　かみたちも
「おかあさま　もういちど　めを　あけて」
「おこえを　きかせて」と
なき　さけびました。

なみさまは　めを
さましませんでした。

THE BIRTH OF THE GOD OF FIRE
When Izanami gave birth to the god of fire,
She was badly burnt, and died.
Izanagi and the other deities cried:
"Oh! Mother, Please once again open your eyes!"
"Let us hear your lovely voice!"
But Izanami did not move.

なぎさまは　どうしても
なみさまに　あいたくて
とおい　みちを　あるいて
くらい　くにに　いきました。

Izanagi, so fond of Izanami, and unable to bear being without her,
Went on a long journey to the far-off land of darkness.

くらい くに （1）

やっと あえた いざなみさまに いざなぎさまは いいました。
「さあ かえろう あかるい くにに」

「この くにの かみに きいて くるから
ここで まっていてね」

ところが いくら まっても
なみさまは こないので
なぎさまは くらい くにに
はいって いきました。

THE LAND OF DARKNESS (1)
"Finally! I have found you…" said Izanagi.
"Let us go back to the land of light together" he said.
"I can't without the permission of the god of this land.
Please wait while I ask." she replied.
He waited and waited but she did not return.
Desperately, Izanagi searched for Izanami in the land of darkness.

おにが　おいかけて　きました。
なぎさまは　にげながら
かみのけをしばっていた
つるを　なげました。

ぶどうの　きが　はえ
ぶどうの　みが　なり
おにが　ぶどうを　たべるまに
なぎさまは　にげました。

くしを　なげると
たけのこが　はえ
おにが　たけのこを
たべるまに　にげました。

Demons chased him.
When he threw his headband at the one of them,
A grapevine full of fruit suddenly appeared;
And Izanagi could quietly slip away
while the demons were eating the grapes.
And then, Izanagi threw down his comb.
In that place bamboo shoots appeared.
Again the demons chasing him stopped to eat,
and he was able to escape.

いざなぎさまは
くらいくにの　でぐちまで　にげて　きました。

くらい　くに　（2）

もものきが　ありました。
「ももさん　たすけてね」
なぎさまは　ももの　みを
おにたちに　なげつけたので
にげて　いきました。

なぎさまは
くらい　くにの　でぐちを
おおきな　いしで
ふさいで　しまいました。

いざなみさまも　おいかけて　きました。
「かなしい　けれど
もう　いっしょに
かえれない　ごめんね」

「ごきげんよう
ありがとう」
「さようなら」

THE LAND OF DARKNESS (2)
When Izanagi arrived at the exit of the land of darkness,
There was a peach tree.
"Help! Help! Oh peach..."He shouted.
Izanagi took some fruit and threw it at the demons
and was able to escape.
Izanagi blocked the door of the land of darkness with a big boulder.
Izanami ran to him.
"It is sad, I know, but I beg you,we cannot be together."
"Be well and take care of yourself," he said.
They bid each other farewell.

さんにんの　かみさま

くらいくにから　かえった　いざなぎさまは
かわの　みずで　からだを　あらいました。

ひだりの　めを　あらいました。
あたりが　ひかり　かがやいて
みこが　おうまれに　なりました。

「おお！　うちゅうを　てらす　あまてらすさま！
しあわせのかみ　あまてらすさま！」

みぎの　めを　あらうと
よるの　せかいを　てらす
つきの　かみが　うまれました。

はなを　あらうと
ちきゅうの　かみ
すさのおさまが　うまれました。

「すばらしい　よいこを　さずかった！」
いざなぎさまは　よろこびました。

THE THREE GODS

When Izanagi returned from the land of darkness,
He washed his body in the river.
When he washed his left eye;
All around him became brilliantly light.
And a new deity came into being.
"Oh! Amaterasu, the god of Happiness was born!!!"
Then, when Izanagi washed his right eye,
The Moon God was born.
When Izanagi washed his nose;
Susanoo, the God of the Earth, was born.
"Wonderful children I have!" Izanagi was full of joy.

すさのおさま

　　ところが　すさのおさまは
　　おおごえで　ないてばかり。

「おかあさま！　ああーん　ああーん」
くちひげが　はえ　あごひげが　ながく　のびても　ないてばかり。

　　なぎさまは　おこって　いいました。
　　「わがままを　いうこは
　　くらい　くにに　いってしまえ！」

　　すさのおさまは　そとへ　でて
　　のはらでないていました。

おそらに　うかんだ　くもが　いきます。
「そうだ　ぼくも　いこう
やさしい　おねえさま
あまてらすさまの　ところへ」

すさのおさまは　ちきゅうを　ぬけだし
おそらに　のぼって
いきました。

THE GOD SUSANOO

Susanoo cried and cried without stop,
"Mamma, Mamma!"
Even when he was big enough to have a moustache and beard,
He just kept on crying.
Izanagi became angry and said:
"A selfish child like that should go to the land of darkness!"
Susanoo went outside to the fields and continued to cry.
He saw clouds floating in the sky, and said:
"I will go where my kind sister, the Sun Goddess Amaterasu, is..."
Susanoo leaped up to the heavens.

あまてらすさま

「おねえさまに　あえて　うれしいです」

すさのおさまは　もっていた　つるぎを
あまてらすさまに　わたしました。

あまてらすさまは　うけとった　つるぎに
ぷっと　いきを　ふきかけました。

しろい　きりが　かかり
さんにんの　おんなの　こが
うまれました。

あまてらすさまは　よろこんで
くびかざりを
すさのおさまに　わたしました。

すさのおさまは　たまを　かんで
ほっぺたを　ふくらませ
ぷうーと　ふきだしました。

しろい　きりの　なかに
ごにんの　おとこの　こが　うまれました。

The Sun Goddess AMATERASU
"I am so happy to meet you, my dear sister."
Said Susanoo, handing a sword to Amaterasu.
Amaterasu took the sword and blew on it.
A white mist appeared and three goddesses were born.
Amaterasu was pleased and gave her necklace to Susanoo.
When he put one of the jewels in his mouth, his cheeks swelled,
And when he spit it out; five male gods were born in a white mist.

あめの　いわや

すさのおさまは　うれしくて
うまに　のり　はしりまわりました

おこめの　ほも
ふみつけて　しまいました。

はたおりひめが
きものを　つくる　きれを
おっていました。

「とんぱた　とんぱた　とんぱたり」
すさのおさまは　あばれうまを
その　へやに　なげこみました。

はたおりひめは　びっくりして
しんで　しまいました。

ひどい　らんぼうに
あまてらすさまは　いしのへやの　あめのいわやに
はいって　しまわれました。

うちゅうが　みんな
まっくらやみに　なって　しまいました。

CAVE IN THE HEAVENS

Susanoo was happily riding his horse.
The horse entered a rice field and trampled the plants.
Woman Hataori was weaving kimono cloth.
"Tonpata tonpata tonpatari"
Susanoo threw the restive horse into the room of the woman.
The woman died from shock.
In protest,
The Sun Goddess Amaterasu retreated into a cave in the heavens,
And the whole universe was plunged into darkness.

ひかりの くに

「ひの かみさま あまてらすさまに はやく
いわやから でて いただこうね」

　　みんな あつまって そうだん しました。
　「いわやの まえで おまつりを しよう」
　　みんなで その よういを しました。

　　　　きを もやし あかるくして
おまつりに つかう
かがみや たまも つくりました。

　　　　　　にわとりも 「こけこっこー」
となきました。

あめのうずめさまが　おどりました。
かみさまたちは　おどりが　おかしくて
おおわらい　しました。

あまてらすさまは　すこし　とを
あけてごらんに　なりました。
ちからもちの　かみが　とを　あけました。

おひさまが　かがやいて
にっぽんは　また
ひかりの　くにに　なりました。

THE COUNTRY OF LIGHT

All the gods gathered to find a way to convince the Sun Goddess
to come out quickly from the cave.
They decided to have a festival in front of the cave.
They prepared for that and burned some woods for a fire.
They made a mirror and a jewel.
The roosters were crying, cock-a-doodle-doo!!!
Ameno-uzume danced a funny dance.
The other gods burst into laughter.
Amaterasu opened the door slightly to see.
The strong god opened the door, and the sun once again shined.
Japan again became a country of light.

おろち　たいじ

すさのおさまは
「ごめんなさい」と　あやまりました。

あまてらすさまは　ゆるして　あげました。
すさのおさまは　いずもの
くにに　おりてきました。

おんなのこ　を　かこんで
おじいさん　おばあさんが
ないていました。

「やっつの　あたまの　ある　おろちが　まいとし　やって　きて
はちにん　いた　おんなのこを　ひとりずつ　たべて　しまい
また　ことしも　やって　くるのです」

すさのおさまたちは　つよい　おさけを　つくり
やっつの　はちに　いれて　おろちを　まちました。

まっかな　めを　ぎらぎらさせて
じひびきを　たてて
おろちは　やって　きました。

おろちは
やっつの　あたまで
おさけをのみ
よっぱらって
ねて　しまいました。

すさのおさまは
「えい　やあ！」と
おろちを　たいじ　して
しまいました。

すさのおさまは　たすけた
おんなのこ　と
けっこんしました。

KILLING THE GIANT SNAKE

Susanoo apologized, and Amaterasu forgave him.
Then Susanoo descended to the land of Izumo in Japan.
With their granddaughter between them,
a man and a woman were crying.
"An eight-headed snake comes every year and eats eight girls one after
the other. Surely it will come again this year."
Susanoo prepared some very strong liquor,
poured it into eight bowls and waited for the eight-headed snake.
The snake appeared with its red eyes shining and a thud.
It drank all the liquor and when it fell into an intoxicated sleep,
Susanoo cut all of its heads off with his sword.
The snake was dead!!! And Susanoo married a girl he saved.

おおくにぬしさま ①

おおくにぬしさまは
すさのおさまの　こどもの　こどもです。

にいさんたちと
いなばの　くにに　いきました。
おおくにぬしさまは　せおった
にいさんたちの　にもつが　おもいので
おくれて　あるいて　いました。

みちの　そばで
けを　むしられた　うさぎが
ないていました。

THE GOD OOKUNINUSHI (1)
Ookuninushi is the grandchild of Susanoo.
He went to a place called Inaba with his brothers.
But because he was carrying a heavy load of brothers,
he was far behind them.
By the roadside a rabbit without fur was crying.

「いたいよー」「どうしたの　うさぎさん」
「むこうの　しまから　いなばに　きたかったの。
ともだちの　かずくらべ　しようと　わにさんを　だまして
ならんだ　わにさんの　うえを　とんできたの。
おこった　わにさんに　あかはだかにされちゃった。
いたいよー　ええーん　ええーん」

「かわいそうに。
けど　だますのは　いけないよ。
かわの　みずで
からだを　あらい
がまの　ほを　しいて
ころがってごらん」

そのとおり　すると
うさぎは　もとの
しろうさぎに　なりました。

"I am in pain!" said the rabbit.
"What happened to you?" asked Ookuninushi.
"I wanted to come to Inaba from the island over there.
I got the sharks to line up and told them
I would count them as part of a game.
I used the chance to jump on their backs and get across the river.
When they realized I was cheating them,
they pulled my fur out; frankly, it hurts terribly…."
"What a pity!! But you shouldn't cheat.
Now, go wash yourself in the river
and then cover your body with ears of bulrush."
The rabbit did exactly as he was told and his fur came back.

おおくにぬしさま (2)

おおくにぬしさま　には
にいさんが　おおぜい　いました。
にいさんたちは　おおくにぬしさまに
いじわるを　しました。

「あかい　いのししを
やまから　おいおろす。
おおくにぬし　それを　つかまえろ」
と　にいさんたちは　おおいしを
ひで　まっかに　やいて
ころがし　おとしました。
したで　まっていた　おおくにぬしさまは
おおやけど　です。

おおくにぬしさまの　おかあさまは
そらの　かみさまに
おねがいしました。
「おおくにぬしの　いのちを　たすけて」

おかあさまは　かいがらの　こなを　おちちで　ねって
やけどに　つけて　なおしました。

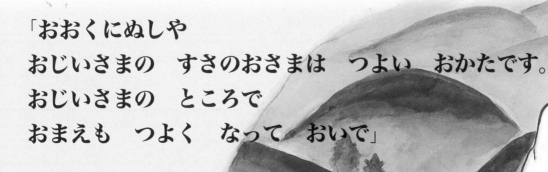

「おおくにぬしや
おじいさまの　すさのおさまは　つよい　おかたです。
おじいさまの　ところで
おまえも　つよく　なって　おいで」

「はい　いってまいります」
「きを　つけてね」
「ごきげんよう
おかあさま」

THE GOD OOKUNINUSHI (2)

Ookuninushi had many brothers who often mistreated him.
One day they said to him:"Go to the bottom of the mountain;
we are going to throw a boar down to you,
and when it comes, catch it."
But instead of a boar they hurled down a red-hot boulder.
Ookuninushi got badly burnt.
When his mother saw him she was shocked.
She begged the god of the heavens to help him.
"Please, save the life of Ookuninushi!!"

She mixed the powder of shell with her
breast milk and rubbed the mixture over his body.
She said, "Dear Ookuninushi,
Your grandfather is very powerful,
so go to him and become powerful, too."
"I will visit him," he said.
"Take care!!"　　"I will⋯."

おおくにぬしさま　（3）

おおくにぬしさまは
とおい　おじいさまの
いえに　つきました。

「おじいさまに　いろいろ
おしえて　もらいなさい
と　かあさまが　いいました」
「よしよし　きたえて　やるぞ」

おおくにぬしさまは
へびが　うようよ　いる　へやに
ねかされました。

「へびが　きたら　ふってね」
かわいい　ひめが　あかい　きれを
そっと　わたして　くれました。

つぎの　よるは
はちと　むかでが　ぶんぶん　ぞろぞろ　いる　へやでした。

ひめが　うすい　きれを　くれました。
おおくにぬしさまは　げんきに　あさを　むかえました。

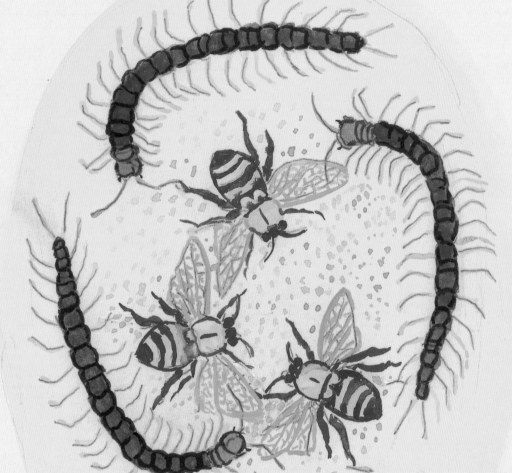

THE GOD OOKUNINUSHI (3)
Ookuninushi finally arrived at the
House of his grandfather far away.
"Grandfather, I am here to learn from you !!" said Ookuninushi.
"I am pleased to teach you." said his grandfather.
Ookuninushi was put into a room full of snakes.
A pretty princess came and handed
him a red cloth saying "When the snakes come,
drive them away with this cloth."
The following night, it was a room full of bees and centipedes.
The princess once again brought him a cloth and saved him.
The following day, Ookuninushi woke up full of energy.

おおくにぬしさま （4）

おじいさんは　おおくにぬしさまを　のはらに　つれだし
ゆみで　やを　とばして
「とんでいった　やを　ひろってこい」と　いいました。
くさ　ぼうぼうの　のはらです。
おおくにぬしさまは　やを　さがしました。

たいへん！
まわりの　くさが　もえだしました。

ねずみが　きて
おしえて　くれました。
「うちは　ほらほら
そとは　すぶすぶ」

おおくにぬしさまは
あしの　したの　ほらあなに
おちて　たすかりました。

「やの　はねは
こねずみが　たべちゃった」
やも　ねずみが
みつけて　くれました。

げんきで　かえった　おおくにぬしさまに
ひめは　よろこびました。

THE GOD OOKUNINUSHI (4)

The god Ookuninushi was taken to a field by
his grandfather who shot an arrow and said,
"Go and bring back the arrow!"
As Ookuninushi was searching for the arrow,
the field of grass and sticks around him suddenly burst into flame.

A mouse came out and said,
"May the outside be grainy and the inside be empty space!!"
Ookuninushi fell into the hole and was saved.
Though the small mouse had nibbled the feather on the arrow,
The mouse brought the arrow to him.
Ookuninushi went cheerfully
home and the princess was deeply pleased.

ちいさな　かみさま

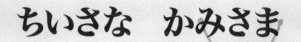

おおくにぬしさまは
いずもの　かみさまに
なりました。

あるひ　うみの　むこうから
きのみの　ふねに　のった
ちいさな　かみが　きました。

「あれは　すくなびこなさま。
おおくにぬしさまを　たすけようと
おそらの　かみが　よこされたのです」
たんぼの　かがしが　おしえました。

A SMALL DEITY
Ookuninushi became the god of Izumo.
One day, a small deity rowing a boat of nut came
from the other end of the ocean.
"That is Sukunabikona;
the god of the heavens might have sent him to help Ookuninushi,"
the scarecrow taught him.

すくなびこなさまは
やまに　きを　うえ
かわに　はしを　かけ
うまや　うしをかうことも
おしえてくれました。

みんなを　よろこばせて
おそらに　かえって　いきました。
あわの　くきを　ばねにして
ぴゅーんと　はねとばして。

Sukunabikona planted trees on the mountains,
built bridges over the rivers,
and also taught the people how to keep horses and cows.
After making everyone happy, he went back to heaven.
Using a millet stalk as a lever, huuuu-uu-u !! he leaped up.

みっつの　たからもの　(1)

あまてらすさまは　そらから　にほんを　ごらんに　なり
かんがえられました。
「いえも　きものも　できた。おこめも　よく　できる。
だけど　よくばり　いじわるが　いるね。
みんなが　うれしいね　ありがとうの
しあわせの　くにに　したいな」

そこへ
ににぎさま　という
かしこい　おまごさまが
うまれました。

THE THREE TREASURES (1)

The Sun Goddess Amaterasu watched
Japan from heaven, and thought:
"Houses and clothes are being made;
rice is also being nicely harvested.
But avarice and wickedness prevail.
I want to create a country where
everyone can enjoy happiness

あまてらすさまは
ににぎさまが　おおきく　なるまでに
おおくにぬしさまと
なかよく　はなしあう　かみさまを
なんにんもそらから　おくりました。

なかには　きじどりも
かみなりさんも　いました。

in their hearts."
A very clever grandchild
named Ninigi was born.
Waiting for Ninigi to grow up,
Amaterasu sent many
gods from heaven to
Ookuninushi,
a pheasant and thunder are also sent.

みっつの　たからもの　(2)

ににぎさまは　おおきくなり
おおくにぬしさまも　よろこんで
おむかえ　することに　なりました。
あまてらすさまは　ににぎさまに
みっつの　たからものを　あげました。
かがみと　たまかざりと　つるぎです。

「かがみは
　うつくしい　こころを
　わすれないでね。

たまかざりは　みんな
みんな　かみさまの　いのちで
つながってるから　なかよしにね。

つるぎは　よいことを　するには
ゆうきが　いることも　あるよ」

「はい　ありがとう」
くもにのって　しゅっぱつしました。
からだの　おおきな　さるたひこさまが
おむかえに　きました。

THE THREE TREASURES (2)

Ninigi grew up; Ookuninushi gladly welcomed him.
Amaterasu gave Ninigi three valuable treasures - a mirror,
a jewel and a sword.
"With the mirror, do not forget your lovely heart;
With the Jewel,
be in good harmony with all attached to the spirit of god;
With the sword,
you will have the courage to stand for the good!!"
"Thanks so much."
He boarded a cloud and left.
The giant Sarutahiko came to welcome him.

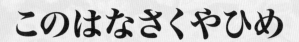

このはなさくやひめ

ににぎさまは
きゅうしゅうの　たかい　やま
たかちほに　おりられました。

あるひ　ににぎさまは
さくらが　さいている
やまを　さんぽしました。

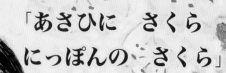

「あさひに　さくら
にっぽんの　さくら」

THE PRINCESS KONOHANASAKUYA

Ninigi landed on Takachiho Mountain in Kyushu.
One day, he took a stroll around
the mountain to look at cherry blossoms.
"The cherry blossoms in the morning sun,
the cherry blossoms of Japan!"

はなの　なかで　かわいい　ひめが
うたって　いました。

やまの　かみの　ひめ
このはなさくやひめ　でした。
ににぎさまは　ひとめで
ひめが　すきになり
けっこんしました。

さんにんの　おとこのこが
うまれました。
いちばん　うえの　みこは
うみさちひこ
いちばん　したは
やまさちひこ　といいました。

A very beautiful princess was singing in the trees.
It was princess Konohanasakuya,
daughter of the mountain god.
Ninigi approached the princess and
fell in love with her.
They married and gave birth to three sons.
The first born was named Umisachi-hiko and
the last born Yamasachi-hiko.

うみさち　やまさち ⑴

うみさちは
うみの　さかなを　とるのが
じょうず　でした。

あるひ　ふたりは
つりばりと　ゆみやを
とりかえっこ　しました。

やまさちは
やまの　けものを　とるのが
じょうず　でした。

ところが　やまさちは
うみさちから　かりた
つりばりを
なくして　しまいました。

「ごめんね　はりを　ごひゃっぽん　かえすから」
「だめだ　あの　はりを　かえせ」
やまさちは　こまって　ないていました。

「なぜ　ないて　いるの」
しおつちの　おじいさんかみが
きくので　わけを　はなしました。

「この　ふねに　おのり。
うみの　かみが　ちゃんと　してくれるから」
やまさちを　のせた　ふねを
しおつちさまは　とんと　おしだしてくれました。
やまさちは　うみの　かみの　ごてんに　つきました。

UMISACHI-HIKO AND YAMASACHI-HIKO(1)

Umisachi-hiko was good at catching fish in the sea.
And Yamasachi-hiko was good at hunting.
One day, they exchanged their hook and bow.
Unfortunately, Yamasachi-hiko lost the hook he borrowed from
Umisachi.
"I am sorry, but I am willing to give you back five hundred
other new hooks instead."
"No, I want only my hook back." replied Umisachi.
Then Yamasachi started crying.
"Why are you crying ?" asked the old god
Shiotsuchi and he listened to the story.
"Board this boat and go to the sea,
then the god of the sea will find that hook for you.
Don't worry!"
He boarded the boat and Shiotsuchi pushed him on his way.
He arrived at the palace of the god of the sea.

うみさち　やまさち （2）

うみの　かみは
うみの　さかなを　みんな　あつめて
つりばりを　さがさせました。

あかたいの　あごに　ささっていた　はりを
やまさちに　かえしました。
わにの　せに　のって　やまさちは　かえり
うみさちに　つりばりを　かえしました。

やまさちと　けっこんしていた
うみの　かみの　ひめも
やまさちの　ところへ　きて
うみべで　みこを　うみました。

UMISACHI-HIKO AND YAMASACHI-HIKO(2)

The god of the sea gathered
together all the fish and
had them search for the hook.
They found it in the chin of a red
seabream.
The god of the sea gave it to
Yamasachi-hiko.
After expressing his gratitude to
the god of the sea,
Yamasachi-hiko got on the back of
a crocodile
and came back to the land.

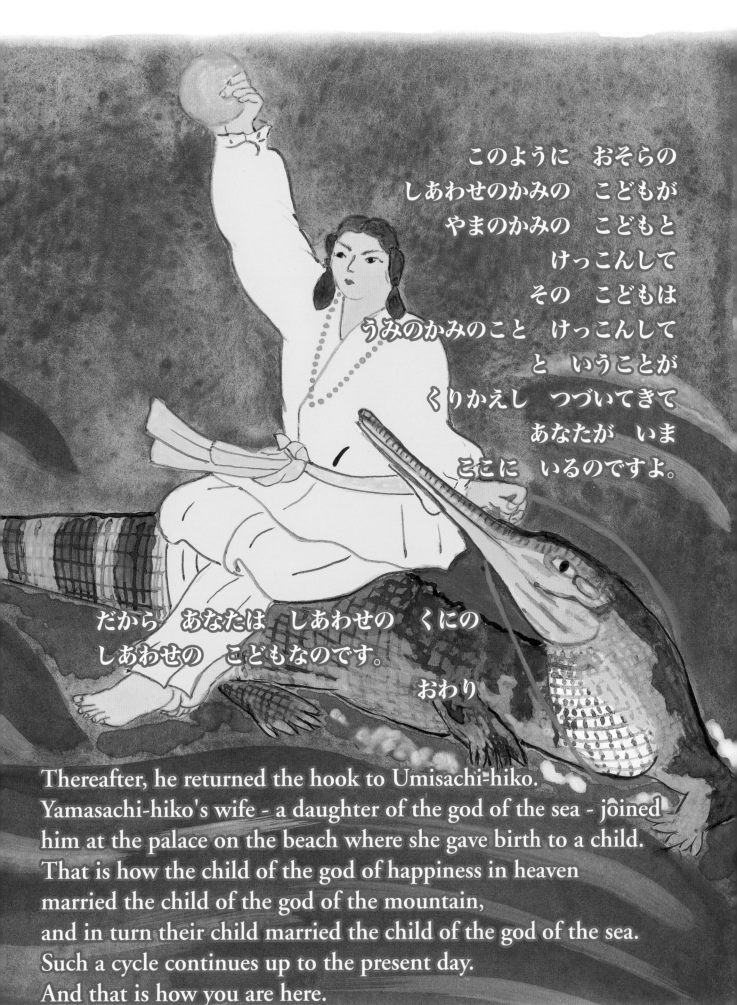

このように　おそらの
しあわせのかみの　こどもが
やまのかみの　こどもと
けっこんして
その　こどもは
うみのかみのこと　けっこんして
と　いうことが
くりかえし　つづいてきて
あなたが　いま
ここに　いるのですよ。

だから　あなたは　しあわせの　くにの
しあわせの　こどもなのです。

おわり

Thereafter, he returned the hook to Umisachi-hiko.
Yamasachi-hiko's wife - a daughter of the god of the sea - joined
him at the palace on the beach where she gave birth to a child.
That is how the child of the god of happiness in heaven
married the child of the god of the mountain,
and in turn their child married the child of the god of the sea.
Such a cycle continues up to the present day.
And that is how you are here.
This is the reason why you are a blessed
child in a country of happiness.   END

「にっぽんの　かみさまの　おはなし」を書きおえて

　ご自分のお子さまが、ずっとずっと一生、
幸せであるようにと願わぬ親はいないでしょう。
　ところが今は、知恵の樹の実をたべすぎて、
親自身もそれがわからなくなってしまっているのが実状です。
　皆さまの古代のご先祖さまは、
人間が幸せに生きることの出来る極意を、しっかりと自分のものにしていました。
　「にっぽんの　かみさまの　おはなし」をくりかえし読むことによって、
まず、お父さま、お母さまが神話の中の神さまたちから、
人生を幸せに生きるヒミツを伝授されるでしょう。
幸せの青い鳥を手にいれることが出来るのです。
　まだ自分で読めないお子さまには、くりかえし読んできかせることによって、
魂のそこにすでにある幸せの根っこが養分を吸いあげて太くたくましくなり、
どんな苦難もよろこびのりこえて、
幸せに生き続けることが出来るように大きくなるのです。
　世界各国の神話を精神医学の見地から解読してきた、

"TALES OF JAPANESE GODS"

I do not believe that there is any parent who does not wish for everlasting happiness for his or her children. However, nowadays, we have acquired too much knowledge and as consequence, we even forget our individual personality. All your ancestors had consistently observed the fact that human beings can live in full happiness. By reading "Tales of japanese gods" parents will understand the secret of leading a happy life from the tales of gods and should introduce the stories to their children. This will enable them to feel happiness and be strong no matter what the difficulties they face. Dr. Daniel Freeman of the American Association of Psychoanalysts who has studied the legend of many countries from a psychiatric point of view declared that in "Tales of japanese gods" the shared consciousness of the Japanese people is expressed, therefore when mothers repeatedly talk about this to their children, there will be a mutual heart to heart love, and the children can quickly learn how to be good children. "Tales of japanese gods" is always the same for every generation because of its attachment to the principles of the universe about happiness. Japan was built accordingly to such principles, and those principles are clearly described in this book. To all the children, I pray for you to grow up cheerfully. For those who would like to know more about the legend of Japan, I recommend them the book; "Tales of japanese gods that textbooks do not teach". (published by Sankei Shinbunsha and Fusousha),and for the truth about the foundation of Japan,the book"Emperor Jimmu whom textbooks do not teach". I personally convey my best regards to the publishers as well as to my dear readers.

Aki Izumoi　August 1999

アメリカの精神分析協会のドクター、ダニエル・フリーマンも、
「にっぽんの　かみさまの　おはなし」には日本民族共通の意識が語られているから、
お母さまがくりかえし語りきかせることによって、
心と心のつながりが心の底に植えつけられていき、
どんなことをすればよい子なのかが自ずとわかっていくのだと話されていました。
　「にっぽんの　かみさまの　おはなし」には、いつまでも、どんな時代にも
変わることのない天地と共に続いていく幸せの法則（真理）が語られています。
私たちの国「日本」は、その法則にのっとって建国された
すばらしい国であることも書かれています。
お子さま方が、ありがたい国に生まれた幸せにも感謝して、
すくすくと明るく成長されることを祈ります。
　もっとくわしく「日本の神話」をお知りになりたい方は
「教科書が教えない日本の神話」（産経新聞社・扶桑社）をお読み下さい。
また、わが国建国の真実は、「教科書が教えない神武天皇」に書かれています。
産経新聞社、扶桑社の方々のあたたかいご声援にささえられて
描きおえることが出来ました。本当に有難うございました。

平成十一年盛夏　　　出雲井　晶

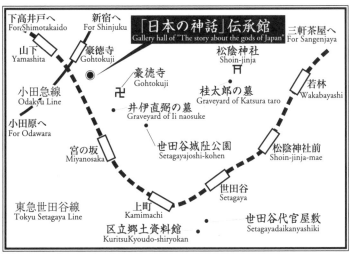

「日本の神話」伝承館
毎週土曜日のみ開館（午前10時～午後4時）。
入館無料。東京都世田谷区豪徳寺1ノ18ノ20。
小田急線豪徳寺駅または東急世田谷線山下駅下車徒歩3分。
豪徳寺商店街の精肉店「石川屋」を左折、
最初の交差点を左折すぐ。
☎03・3427・0007。駐車場なし。

Gallery hall of "The story about the gods of Japan"
Ms. Izumoi operates a gallery hall open to the public on
Saturdays from 10:00A.M to 4:00P.M.

It is 3minutes from Goutokuji station on Odakyu Line or
Yamasita station on Tokyu Setagaya Line.
Turn left at the meat shop Ishikawaya in the shopping center
of Goutokuji and find it on your left at the first intersection.
Admission is free but no parking is available.

Address:Goutokuji 1-18-20, Setagaya-ku, Tokyo-to
TEL:03-3427-0007

出雲井 晶（いずもい・あき）

作家、日本画家。

著書に『母と子におくる　教科書が教えない日本の神話』『教科書が教えない神武天皇』など多数。内閣総理大臣賞、文部大臣表彰（1999年）など多くの賞を受賞している。「日本の神話」伝承館館長。

Aki Izumoi is a painter and a writer. Among her works are;"The story about the gods of Japan for mother and child that textbooks do not teach"; "Emperor Jimmu whom textbooks do not teach." She was granted many awards, including The Prime Minister's Award as a painter; the 1999 Ministry of Education's Award for culture. She is the director of a gallary hall of "Tales of japanese gods".

アデュアヨム カンコエ

翻訳家、通訳。

1969年、西アフリカのトーゴに生まれる。1995年、来日。日本語、コンピュータを学ぶ。1999年、株式会社サンシャインに入社。

Jules Kankoe Aduayom is a translator and an interpreter. He was born in 1969 in Togo, West Africa. He came to Japan in 1995. He has studied Japanese language and computer technology. He joined SUNSHINE CO.,LTD in 1999.

にっぽんの　かみさまの　おはなし 英語版
TALES OF JAPANESE GODS

発行日 / First printing	平成12年 6月30日初版第一刷 平成12年 9月30日　第三刷 30-JUNE,2000
著　者 / Pictures and Text by	出雲井　晶 Aki Izumoi
訳　者 / Translated by	アデュアヨム　カンコエ Jules Kankoe Aduayom
発行者 / Publisher	齊藤　繁 Shigeru Saitoh
発　行 / Published by	株式会社　産経新聞ニュースサービス Sankei Shinbun News Service Inc. 株式会社　扶桑社 FUSO PUBLISHING Inc.
発　売 / Distributed by	東京都港区海岸1-15-1 〒105-8070 電話03-5403-8871（編集）03-5403-8859（販売） 1-15-1 Kaigan Minato-ku Tokyo 〒105-8070 Phone03-5403-8871(the editorial staff) 03-5403-8859(the sales staff)
印刷・製本 / Printed by	日本プリンテクス株式会社 NIPPON PRINT AND GRAPHICS INC.

©2000 Izumoi Aki/Jules Kankoe Aduayom Printed in Japan,ISBN4-594-02920-5 C8795